minimalist
Fashion Portfolio Sketchbook
ABSTRACT FIGURE DRAWING TEMPLATES
style "Alina"
by Irina V. Ivanova

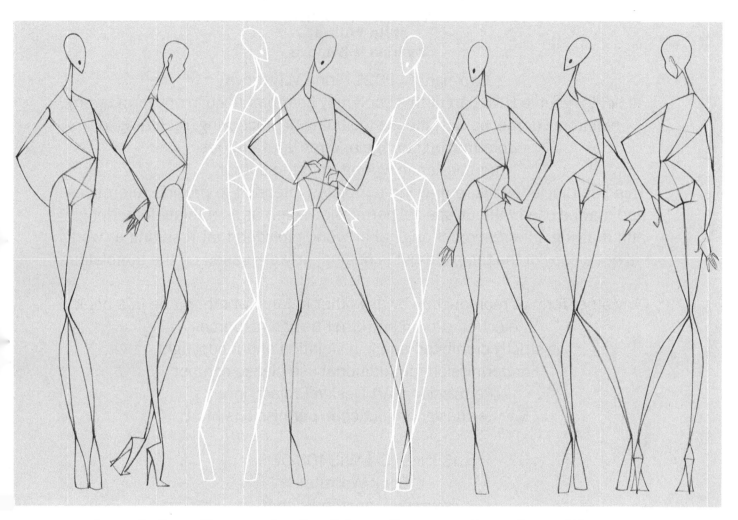

- six minimalist style fashion figures for sketching
- single (one per page) figures as well as groups of two figures per page
- torso fashion templates
- groups of multiple croquis figures
- selection of different scale and size of templates
- all templates are printed in gray color
- three-quarter, front, back, and side views included
- mild movement and still poses

**minimalist
Fashion Portfolio Sketchbook
ABSTRACT FIGURE DRAWING TEMPLATES
style "Alina"
by Irina V. Ivanova**

ISBN: 978-1-953408-07-5
Book Website
www.fashioncroquis.com
Email: contact@artdesignproject.com

Give feedback on the book at:
contact@artdesignproject.com

Art Design Project, Incorporated
Printed in U.S.A

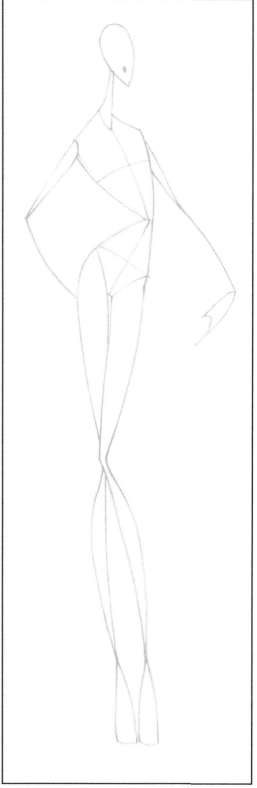

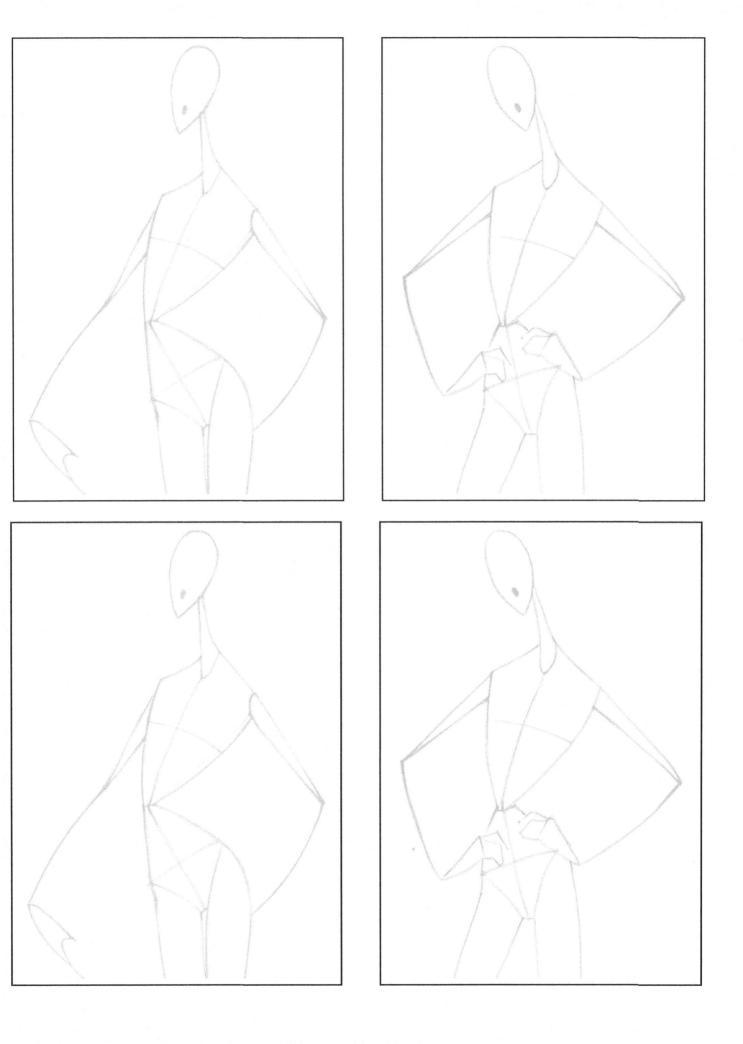

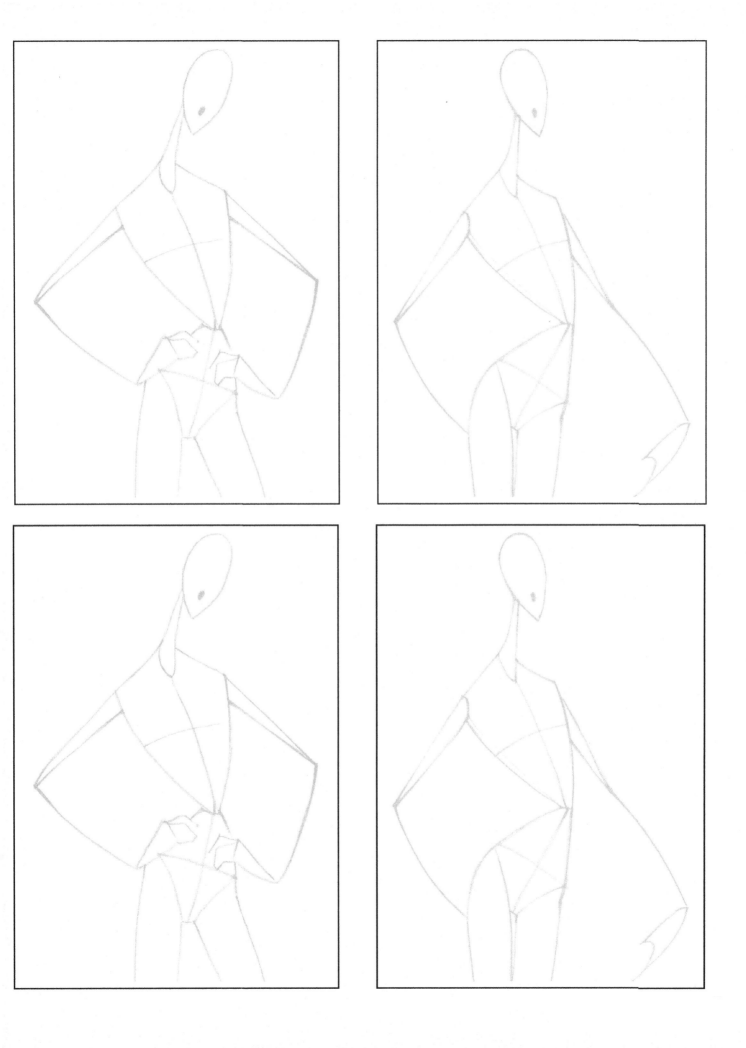

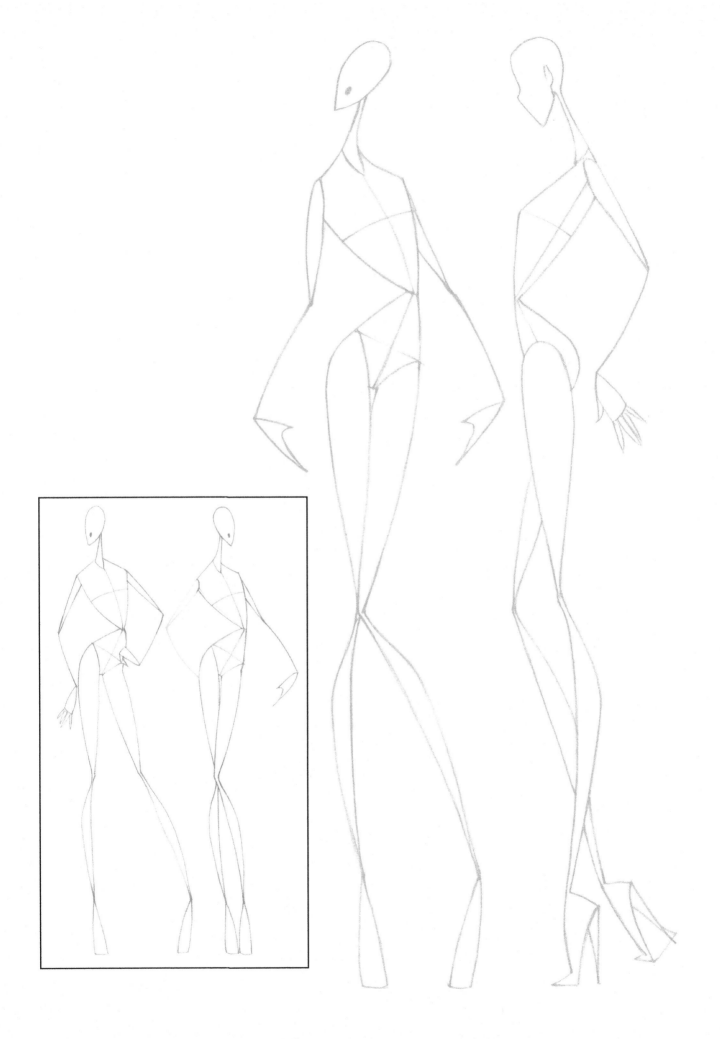

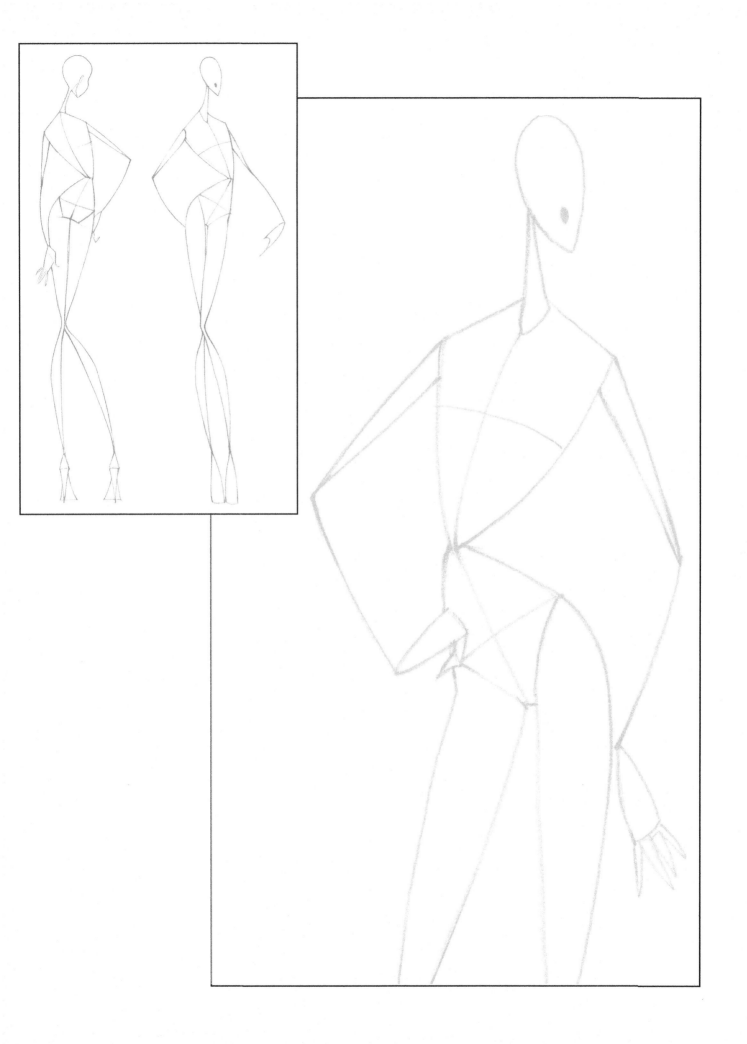

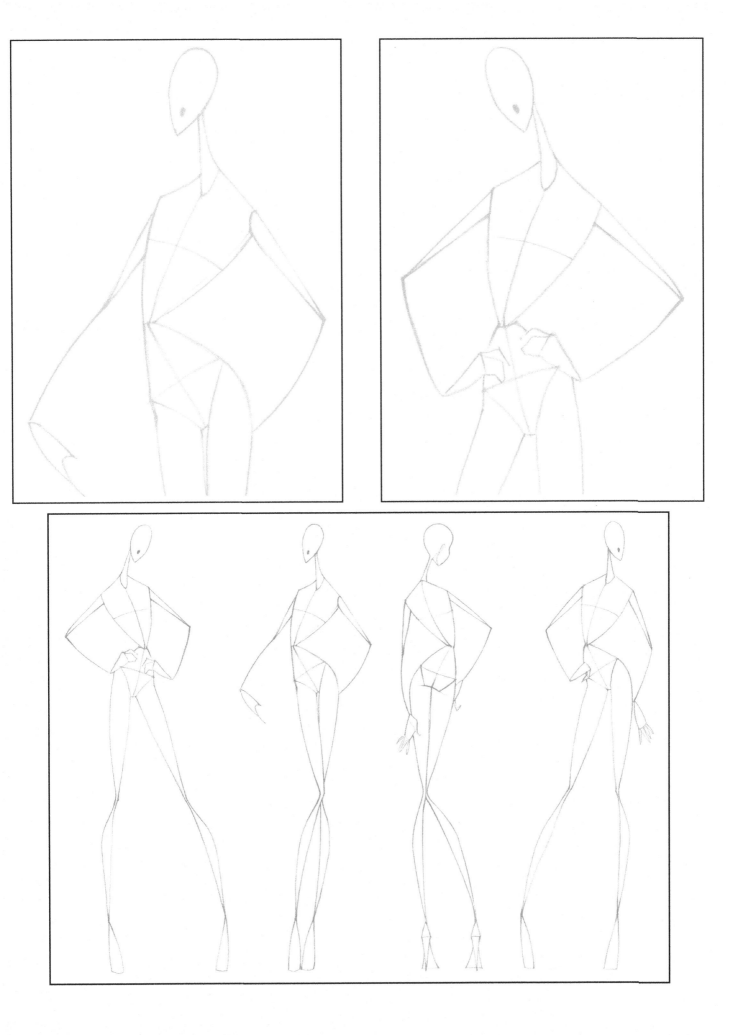

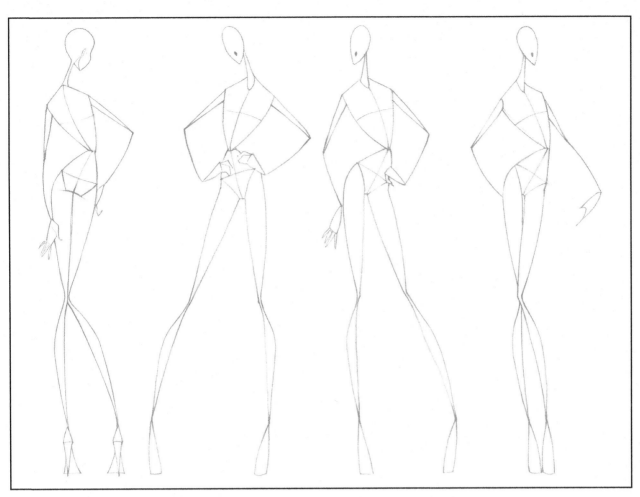

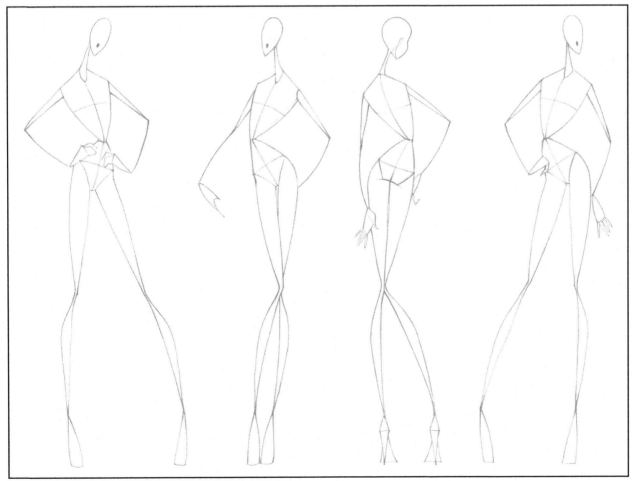

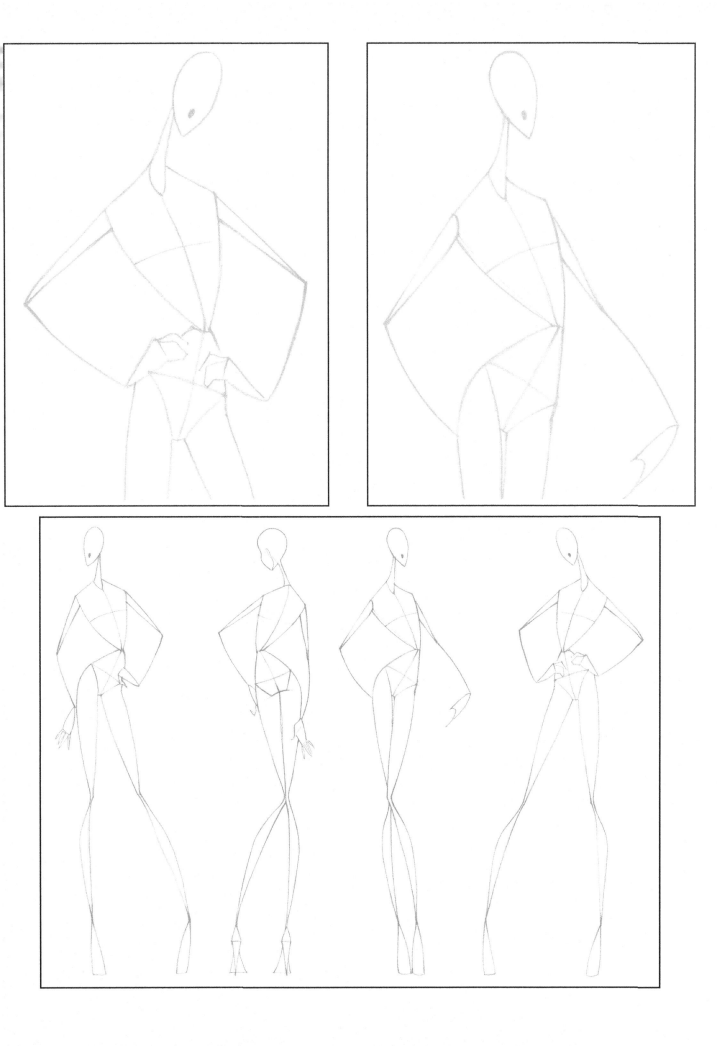

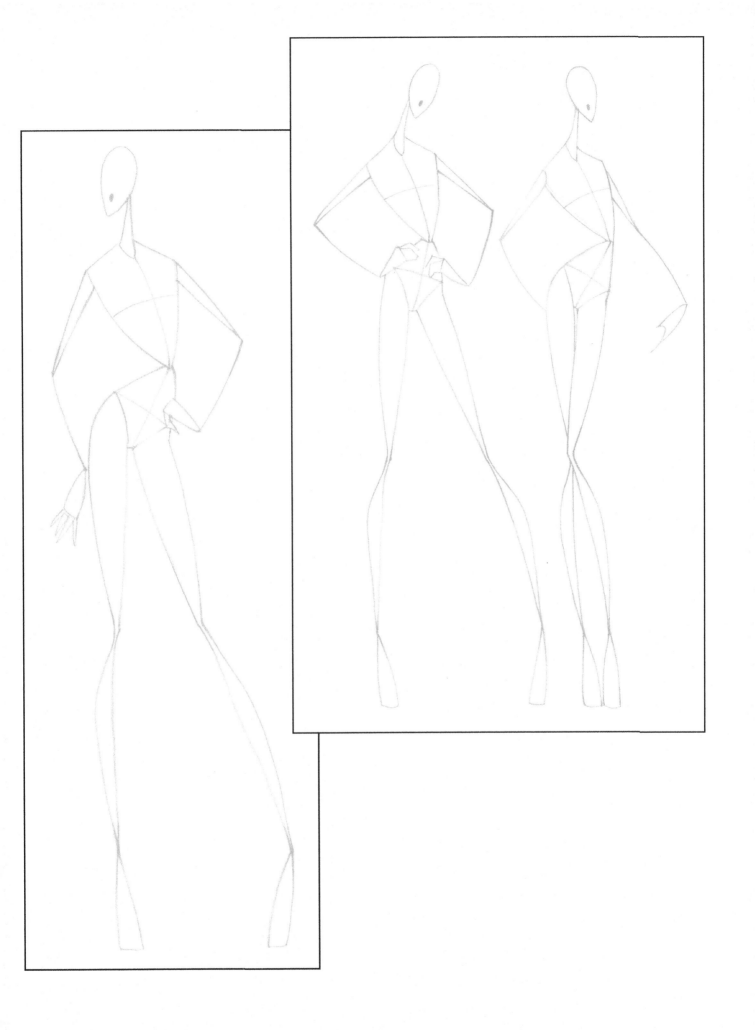

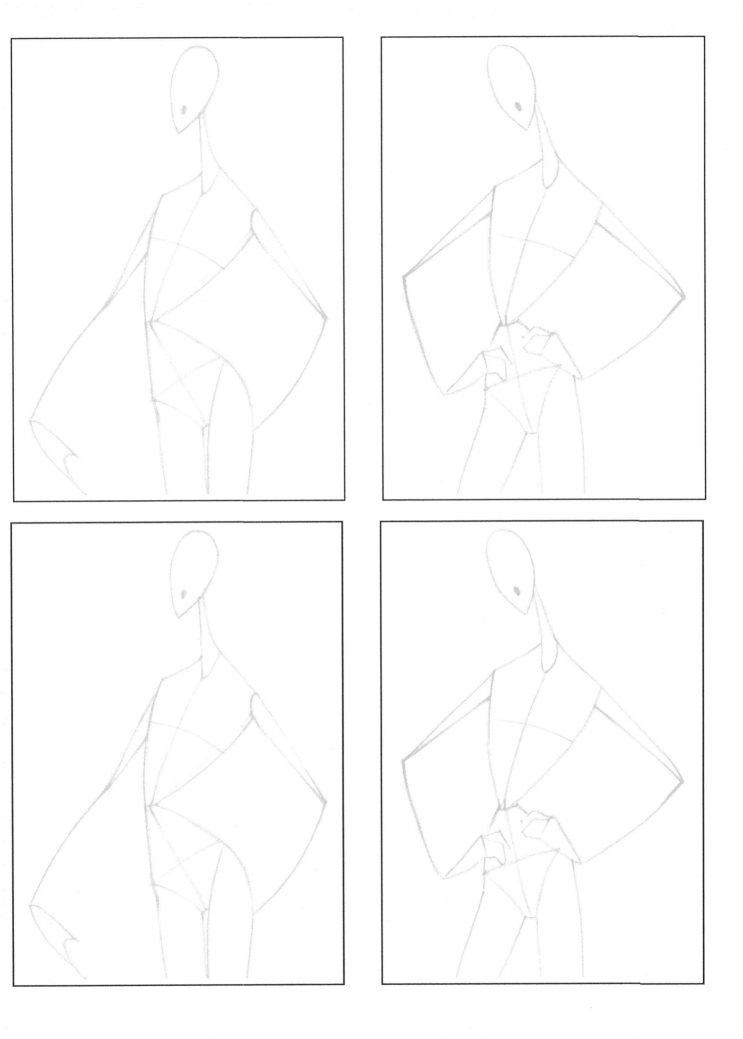

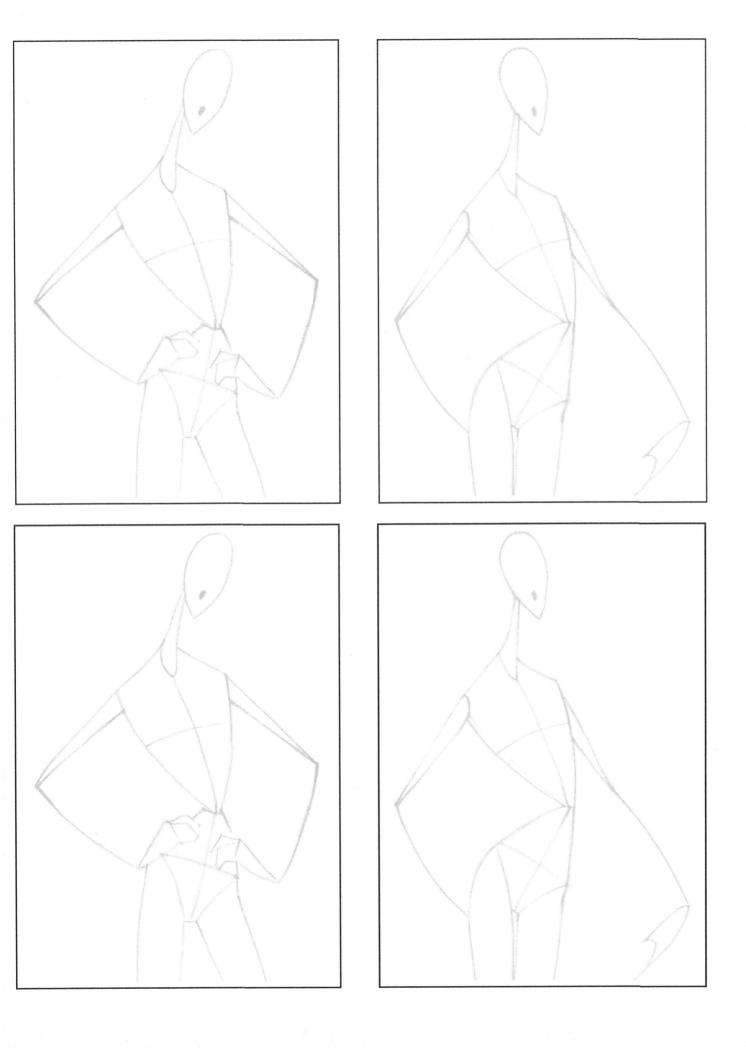

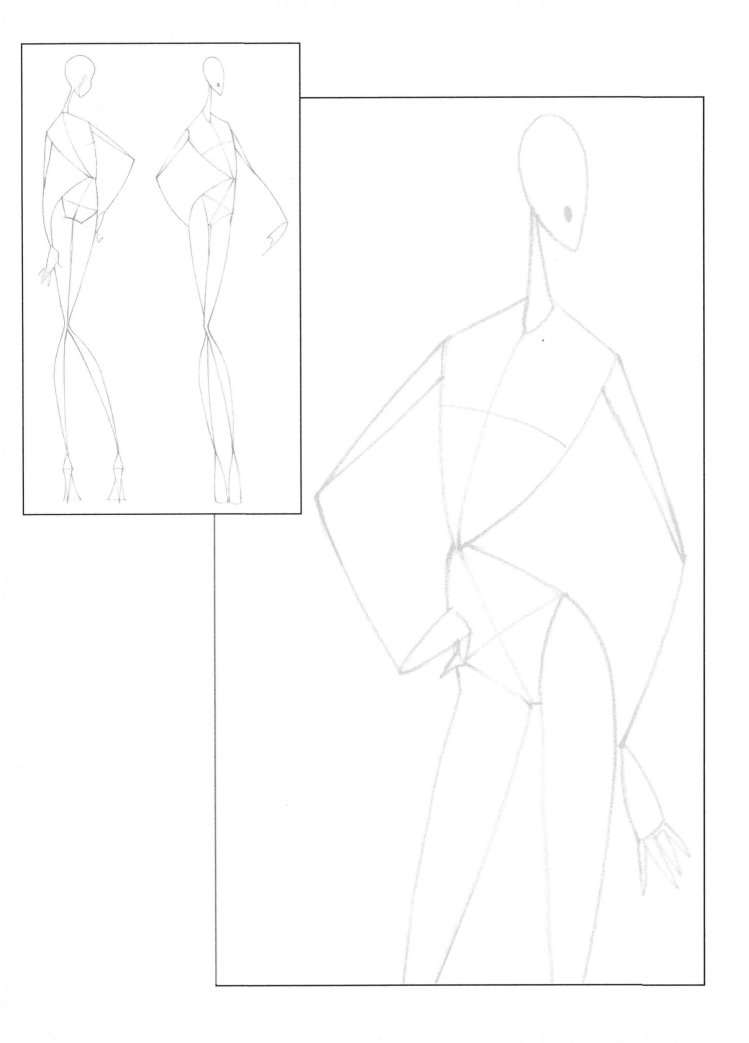

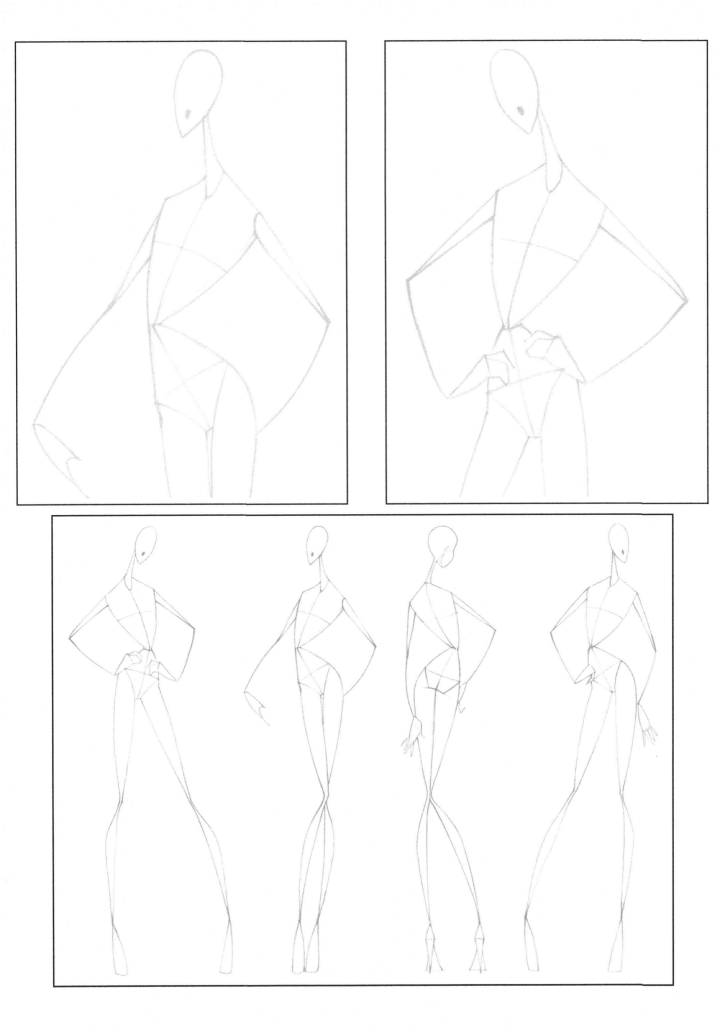

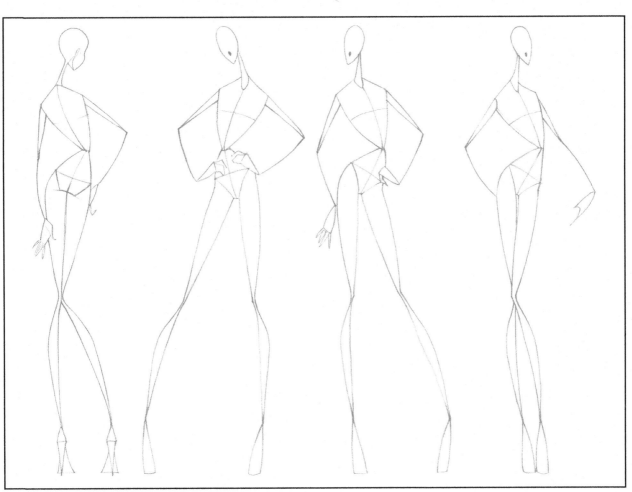
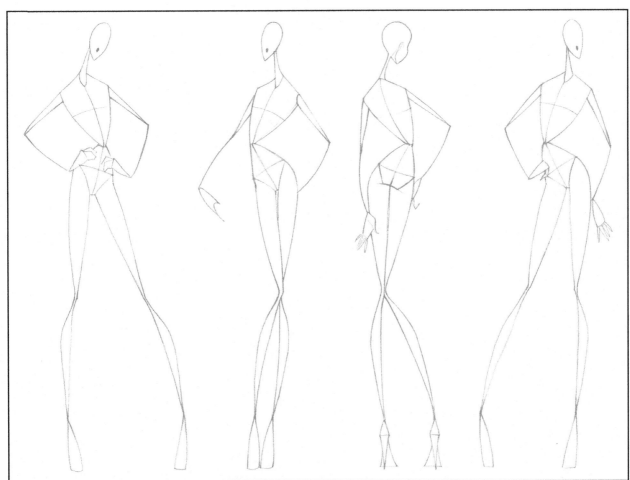

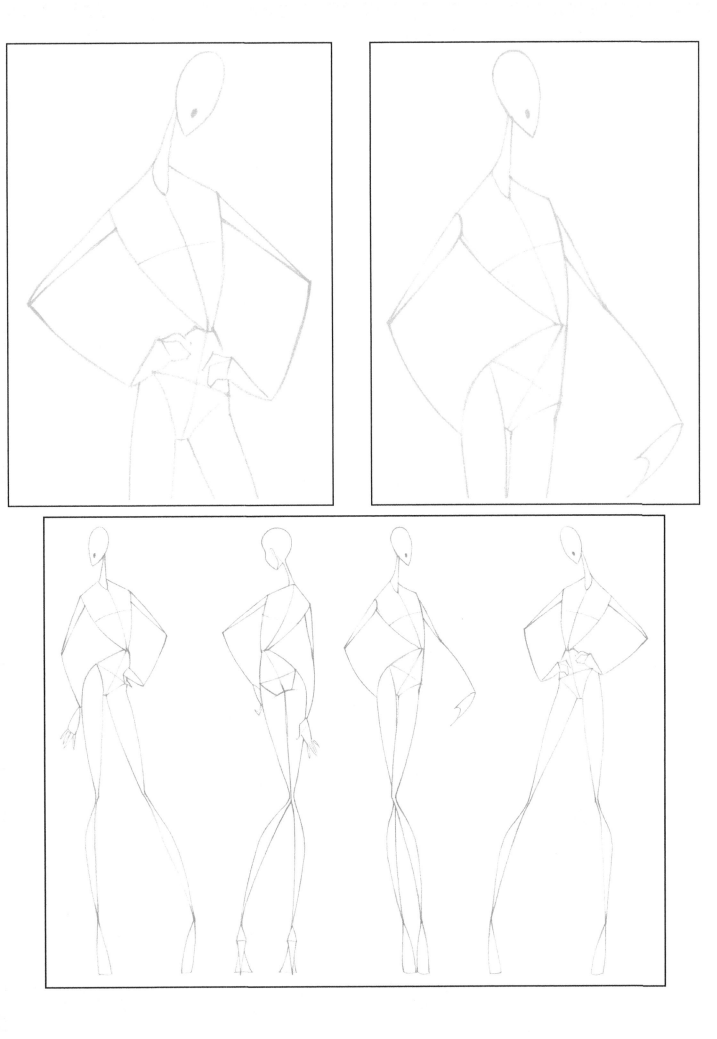

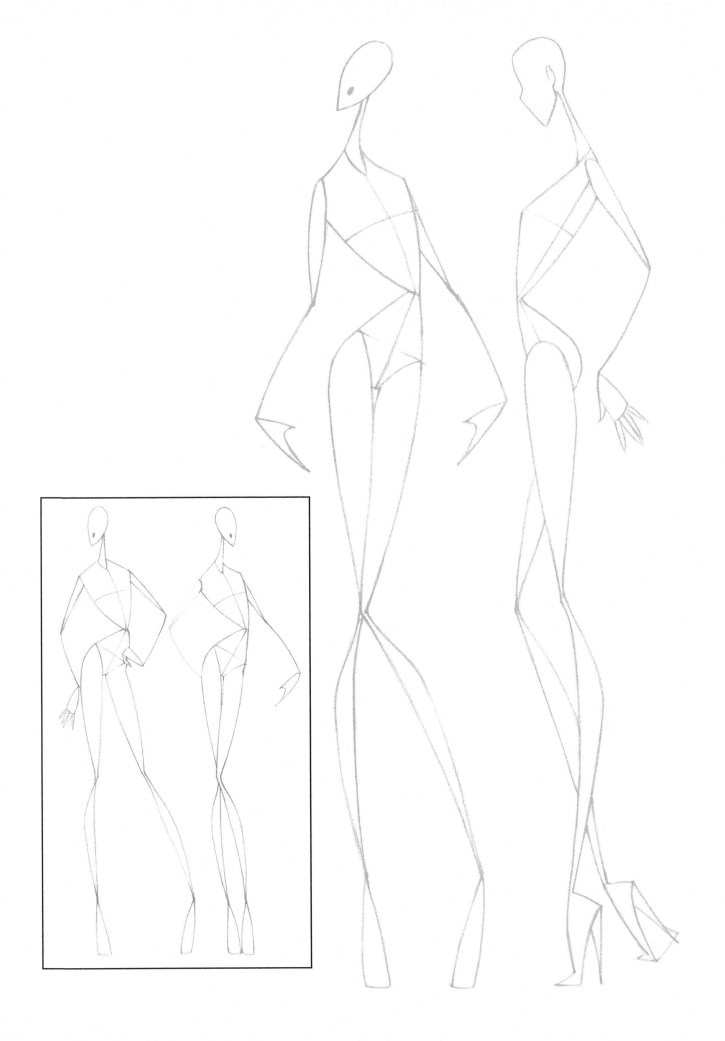

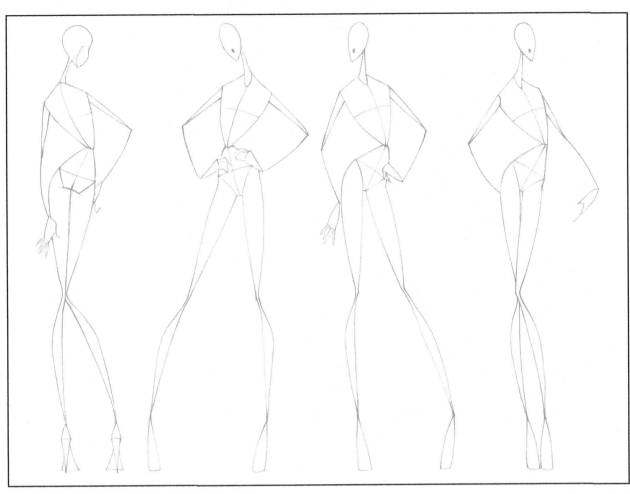

About the author

Irina V. Ivanova

is a Florida-based educator, fashion illustrator, and visual artist. Irina delights in merging her versatile professional life experiences in a blend of fashion, art, and teaching.

As a fashion illustrator, Irina combines her profound knowledge of clothing design with artistry. In her books, Irina balancing creative and technical aspects of fashion process.

Art and fashion merged in Irina's books helping each other for the benefit of a reader.

Irina's books are not just "beautiful" books about fashion. Irina's books are practical guides on fashion subjects and collection of practical resources articulated with artistic talent and illustration skill. Her fashion drawing books are real-world practical and, in the meantime, artistically stylish way.

www.ivanova.studio
www.FashionCroquis.com

stnadadrd style figure   stylized style figure

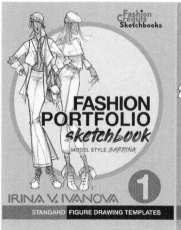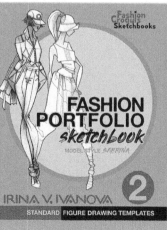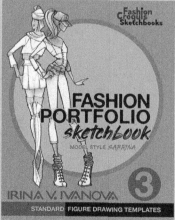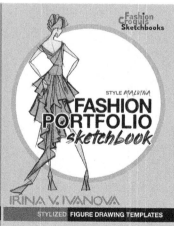

FASHION PORTFOLIO SKETCHBOOKS:
www.fashioncroquis.com/sketch-books

Fashion Design SketchBook

Women's Wear Fashion Illustration Templates
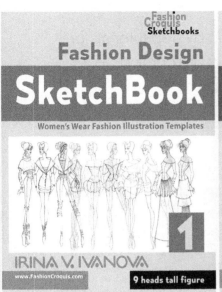

Fashion Croquis Sketchbooks

1
IRINA V. IVANOVA
www.FashionCroquis.com
9 heads tall figure

2
IRINA V. IVANOVA
www.FashionCroquis.com
plus size figure

3
IRINA V. IVANOVA
www.FashionCroquis.com
12 heads tall figure

Fashion Design SketchBook
Men's Wear Fashion Illustration Templates

4
IRINA V. IVANOVA
www.FashionCroquis.com
male figure

Fashion Croquis Sketchbooks

Children's Wear Sketch Book
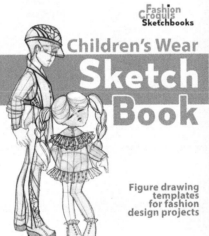
Figure drawing templates for fashion design projects
IRINA V. IVANOVA
www.FashionCroquis.com

Fashion Croquis Sketchbooks

Infant and Toddler Wear Sketch Book
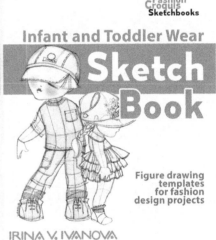
Figure drawing templates for fashion design projects
IRINA V. IVANOVA
www.FashionCroquis.com

Fashion Design Sketch Book
Runway movement

Women's Wear Fashion Illustration Templates

front, side, and 3/4 views
www.FashionCroquis.com
IRINA V. IVANOVA

Fashion Croquis Sketchbooks

Fashion Design Sketch Book
Photoshoot poses
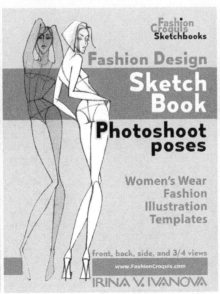
Women's Wear Fashion Illustration Templates

front, back, side, and 3/4 views
www.FashionCroquis.com
IRINA V. IVANOVA

Fashion Croquis Sketchbooks

Fashion Face Sketch Book
Templates for hairstyle and headwear design

front, side, and 3/4 views
www.FashionCroquis.com
IRINA V. IVANOVA

Fashion Croquis Book series

Fashion Croquis " How to draw" books include step by step tutorials for figure drawing and technical drawing: more books are coming.
Sign for updates at www.fashioncroquis.com/signup.html

Fashion Illustration Resources books from the Fashion Croquis Book series include:

- Figure drawing templates
- Drawing step by step tutorials
- Main terms illustrated

...and much more

visit www.FashionCroquis.com to learn about the Fashion Croquis Books

Fashion Croquis Books

Fashion Croquis book is a collection of practical, visual, and easy to use fashion drawing resources.

We create (design and publish) paperback books, eBooks, sketchbooks and downloadable templates for fashion designers.

Croquis products: Fashion illustration, Figure drawing for fashion, Technical drawing for fashion design (fashion Flats)

Our publishing projects include menswear, womenswear, and children's wear design illustration resources.

Sign up for updates: Be the first to be informed about upcoming projects!

The Fashion Croquis Books

Learn fashion drawing with these visual and practical books. Each book includes a set of figure drawing templates for fashion illustration, drawing tutorials, and main fashion clothing terminology. Topics include fashion drawing, fashion illustration, technical drawing, and fashion figure drawing.

Fashion Croquis Sketch Books

Illustrate your project using books with preprinted figure templates.

www.FashionCroquis.com

- **Books**
- **eBooks**
- **Sketch books**
- **Project books: step by step tutorials**
  by Irina V. Ivanova

Paperbooks and eBooks

ISBN-13: 978-0984356065   ISBN-13: 978-0984356058

www.fashioncroquis.com/project-books

eBook Booklets

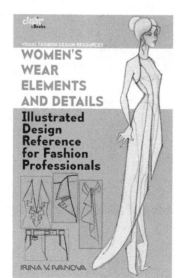

www.fashioncroquis.com/ebooks

Made in United States
North Haven, CT
07 October 2022

25160225R00063